What Others Are Saying

"*Kasey's First Day of Basketball Practice* is a story of courage, preparation, and growing confidence in the face of adversity. Kentrell Martin and Kentrell Martin Jr. guide us through a youngster's love for basketball and his frustrations and challenges with being hard of hearing. This book not only serves to educate people of all ages about basketball, but it also introduces its readers to American Sign Language (ASL)—including some signs associated with the game. At the same time, it lays the foundation to help us all be comfortable in our own skin."

—Buzz Williams, Head Coach, Virginia Tech Men's
Basketball

"What a fun book about a day in the life of a young basketball player. *Kasey's First Day of Basketball Practice* is a terrific tool to teach young aspiring athletes how to deal with differences among peers. This book is tremendous for young people looking to learn and have fun."

—Jamie McNeilly, Assistant Coach, Virginia Tech Men's
Basketball

"Kentrell Martin's description of basketball practice and playing basketball are wonderful! I felt myself enjoying every moment as I read the story."

—Monte Towe, Indiana Basketball Hall of Famer and NC
State National Champion

"Kentrell Martin has done it again! *Kasey's First Day of Basketball Practice* is a great book to introduce young children to the sport of basketball. The book is well thought out yet simple, making it easy for young children to grasp the basic principles of the game. I teach a basketball class on a college campus and will definitely introduce this book to my class. "

—Mark Downey, Assistant Coach, IPFW Men's Basketball

KASEY's First Day of Basketball Practice

Kentrell Martin
& Kentrell Martin Jr.

The Shelly's Adventures Series

Kasey's First Day of Basketball Practice by Kentrell Martin and Kentrell Martin Jr.

ISBN (hardcover): 978-0-9851845-4-4
ISBN (softcover): 978-0-9851845-5-1
ISBN (ebook): 978-0-9851845-6-8
Library of Congress Control Number: 2016901553

Book design by Jill Ronsley, suneditwrite.com
Illustrations by Nguyen Minh Duc
Vector icons in this book designed by Freepik, flaticon.com

Published by Shelly's Adventures LLC
PO Box 2632, Land O Lakes, Fl 34639 USA
www.shellysadventuresllc.com

10 9 8 7 6 5 4 3 2 1

Printed and bound in the USA

Shelly's Adventures LLC was created to provide children and their parents with reading material that teaches American Sign Language. Shelly's Adventures LLC produces materials that make signing fun for kids, parents and teachers.

 https://www.facebook.com/ShellysAdventures

 https://twitter.com/Shellysadventur

Contents

Chapter 1

Today's the Day!

At 8:30, Kasey's alarm clock rang loudly next to his bed, but he didn't move.

"Kasey! Kasey!" His mother's voice was the first thing he heard. "Your alarm has been ringing for a full minute! Wake up!"

Even though Kasey had not heard the alarm, he *had* heard his mother's voice. He sat up quickly, wiping drool off of his mouth with his hand.

"Huh …! What …? When …?" Kasey mumbled as he looked around the room. He saw the alarm on his bedside table and pressed the off button.

He had been up late the previous night thinking about today—his big day! Today was the first day of basketball practice. Every day for a month, Kasey had been preparing by going to the basketball court to practice. Yesterday, he practiced a lot longer than usual.

"Didn't you hear your alarm ringing?" his mom asked.

Kasey rubbed his eyes and answered, "No, I didn't hear the alarm. I was dreaming about basketball practice. Thanks for waking me, Mom. What time is it?"

Before his mother could reply, he looked at the clock. "Never mind! The clock says it's 8:37."

"What time is your basketball practice?" his mom asked.

"It's at 9:30. I don't have much time. I'd better get ready."

As Kasey hopped out of bed, his mom exited the room. From the hallway she yelled back, "When you're ready, hurry downstairs. I cooked you a light breakfast."

Kasey walked quickly to the bathroom and brushed his teeth. Then he put on the clothes that he had laid out the previous night, tied his shoes, and slung his gym bag over his shoulder, containing his armband, headband, and basketball. He grabbed his hearing aid from the dresser and headed downstairs to the kitchen. His mom and dad were sitting at the table eating his mom's famous breakfast sandwiches. There was a sandwich on a plate in front of his chair, but he knew he couldn't eat it right before practice.

"Mom, do we have any bananas?" he asked.

"Yes, we do," she said. "Don't you want the breakfast sandwich I made for you?"

"I do, but not before practice. I need to eat something light."

Before Kasey's mother could respond, his father grabbed the plate in front of the empty chair. "Don't worry! I'll eat it," he said as he opened his mouth and took a big bite.

Kasey and his mother laughed and shook their heads. Kasey headed to the counter to grab a banana. As he peeled it, he glanced at the clock on the microwave. It was 9:00. He only had thirty minutes before practice started. He had to leave right away so that he would have enough time to stretch and warm up.

"Mom, I'm going to the basketball court now," he said.

"Already?" she said. "You still have thirty minutes. The court is only a minute away."

Kasey's father answered for him. "He can't just walk onto the court at 9:30. He needs to warm up and get loose before practice starts."

"He's young! He doesn't need to stretch," said Kasey's mom.

"Bye Mom and Dad. I'll see you later." Kasey kissed his mother on the cheek and headed towards the door with his gym bag over his shoulder.

"Go get 'em, son! Remember, play hard and have fun," his dad yelled.

Chapter 2

Should I Wear It?

While Kasey stood on the curb, waiting to cross the street, he noticed that the sounds of the cars passing and birds chirping weren't as clear as usual. He wasn't wearing his hearing aid! He stopped for a moment to think about whether or not he should go back home to get it or go on without it. He looked at the court across the street and saw that only one little boy had arrived. He decided to get the hearing aid, turned around, and ran home.

As soon as he walked through the door, his mother asked, "What did you forget?"

Kasey pointed to the counter where his hearing aid lay.

His dad turned around. Pointing at the hearing aid, he said, "You're going to need that! How can you pay attention if you can't hear the instructions?"

Kasey shrugged, grabbed the hearing aid, and called out, "Bye!" as he ran back out the door.

By the time he reached the court, four boys were dribbling their balls around the court and shooting baskets. He only knew one of the boys, but they all said hello.

Kasey sat on the sidelines, opened his gym bag, and put on his headband and wristband. He placed his hearing aid on his lap as he tied his shoes tightly. When he was ready to go, he stood up, and his hearing aid fell to the ground. He had forgotten about it that quickly!

He picked up the hearing aid and held it in his hand, unsure whether he wanted to wear it or not. He had no idea how many players he

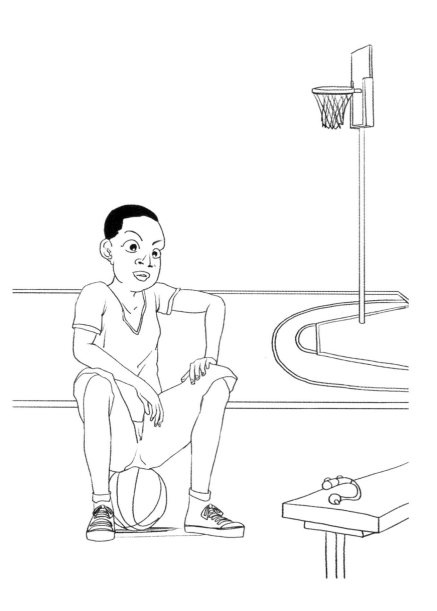

would know on the team, and he didn't want any of the kids to look at him differently.

Kasey decided not to put the hearing aid on. He placed it in his gym bag and took out his basketball. As he ran out onto the court, three more boys arrived. They all warmed up with their basketballs until it was time to start practice.

Chapter 3

A Star in the Making

"Huddle up, everyone!" said the coach. "My name is Coach Towe, and I will be your coach this season. I see a few familiar faces and a lot of new ones. As the players who know me will tell you, I'm a fun coach. I don't ask for much! All that I ask is that you have fun, play hard, and follow directions. If you can do these three things, you're going to be all right.

"Today is going to be easy since it's the first day of practice. I want to see how you all play. We'll do some offensive drills followed by a few defensive drills. That will be it. Does any-one have any questions?"

The players looked around to see who would ask the first question. Kasey, being a brave little boy, raised his hand. "If we score 100 points in our first game, will you take us all out for pizza?" All the kids clapped their hands and cheered!

The coach replied, "100 is a lot of points! Yes, if you are lucky enough to score 100 points, I'll take you all out for pizza."

The team jumped up and down and cheered again, more excited about eating pizza than about the practice.

Once they'd settled down, Coach Towe lined them up for offensive drills—dribbling, shooting, and passing—and watched them intently as they played. Kasey felt good dur-ing all the drills. He was glad he had been practicing them all summer.

At the end of the offensive practice, the coach told them to drink water and prepare for the defensive drills.

Chapter 4

Didn't Hear a Thing

The team ran back to the basketball court and gathered around Coach Towe.

"Are you ready to hear my instructions for the next drill?" he asked. The players all nodded and said "Yes, coach!"

"In the next drill, we're going to practice team defense," said the coach. "I want you all to talk to each other out on the court. If you need help, call for help. Call out the picks. You can't play good defense if you don't talk to each other. Offense sells tickets but defense

wins games. Even if you play good offense, you can't play for me if you can't play defense."

As the players got ready for the defensive drill, Kasey noticed his father sitting on the sideline bench. He wasn't surprised because his father always came to watch him play. This made Kasey happy, and he started the drill full of energy.

It was a four-on-four defensive drill, in which the players call out picks and talk to each other. On the second play of the drill, Kasey's man scored on a layup. Seconds later his man scored again. This made Kasey angry. He turned to his teammate and said, "Call out the picks! Let me know if someone is setting a screen!"

"I did," said his teammate.

Coach blew the whistle to stop them from arguing. "Kasey, you've got to play better defense than that if you want to get any playing time."

Kasey was determined not to let his man score any more points. For the next ten minutes, his man didn't score at all, and Kasey showed that he could play great one-on-one defense. Practice was coming to an end.

"The team that scores the next basket wins the drill!" Coach Towe announced.

Kasey's man dribbled to his right. Kasey chased him, but he stopped as he ran into a guy on offense who had set a pick on him. His man pulled up and shot a jumper that hit nothing but net! Kasey looked at his teammate, disappointed.

His teammate came over to him and said, "I called out the pick! Didn't you hear me?"

Kasey was about to accuse him of lying. Then he remembered that he wasn't wearing his hearing aid. He put his head down and said, "No I didn't hear you!"

Chapter 5

Be Who You Are

As Kasey walked to the sideline, his father held out his hand. In it was Kasey's hearing aid. "Why weren't you wearing your hearing aid?" he said.

Kasey stared at the ground, trying to think of an excuse, but he realized that he had no good reason for not wearing his hearing aid. Instead of making up a lie, he told his father the truth. "I didn't want the boys on the team to look at me as if I was different from them. If I had already met them I would have worn it, but since there were so many new faces, I decided not to put it on."

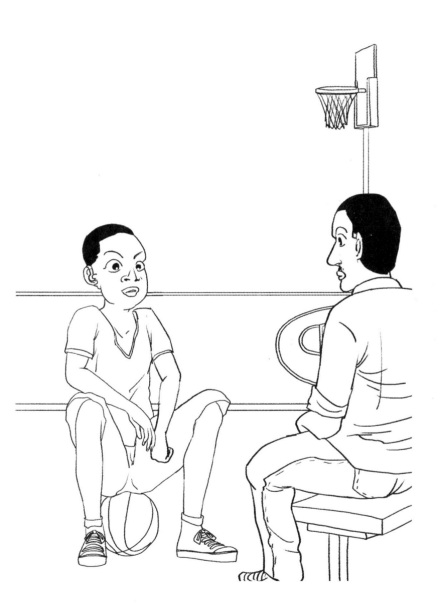

His father replied, "Kasey, different is a good thing! We were all created different from each other. That's the beauty of the world. Even if you never do anything else, promise me that you will always be yourself. The world is full of people who want to be like other people, but the ones who stand out in the world are those who accept who they are. There can never be another Kasey. As you grow up, you will see that the people who care most about you are the ones who appreciate the real you! I promise you, if you show them the real Kasey—the Kasey who wears a hearing aid in his left ear—they will like you better than the Kasey who just wants to fit in." Kasey nodded his head. " Now tell me," said his father, "What lesson did you learn today?"

Kasey replied, "Be yourself!"

"That's right! Now, let's go home and watch the Cleveland Cavaliers play basketball!"

Kasey gave his father a big hug and they walked home to watch the game!

Questions & Answers

Answer the following questions, either aloud or in writing:

1. Why did Kasey want to go to the basketball court early?

2. Why didn't Kasey eat breakfast?

3. What 3 things did Coach Towe ask the players to do at every practice?

4. Why didn't Kasey wear his hearing aid at practice?

5. What lesson did Kasey learn today? Did you learn the same lesson?

Did you know?

Basketball was invented in 1891 by James Naismith.

The first basketball hoop was a peach basket.

The first backboards were made of wire.

Wilt Chamberlain holds the NBA record for the most points scored in a game. (He scored a whopping 100 points!)

The height of a basketball goal is 10 feet.

A high school basketball court is the not the same size as a college or NBA court.

The three-point line on an NBA court is longer than the same line on a college or high school basketball court.

A player is allowed 5 fouls from Little League basketball to college basketball. However, in the NBA, a player is allowed 6 fouls.

The shortest player ever to play in the NBA, Muggsy Bogues, was only 5 feet 3 inches tall.

The tallest man ever to play in the NBA, Gheorghe Muresan, was 7 feet 7 inches tall.

Fun Picks—YOUR Picks vs. MY Picks

1. Who is your favorite basketball player?

2. What is your favorite basketball team?

3. Name your 5 favorite players.

_____, _____,

_____, _____,

_____

4. Who do you think will win the NBA championship this year?

5. Why?

6. Who do you think will win the MVP this year?

Circle your top 5 favorite players by position using the players listed below on pages 22 and 23. Then enter your selections on page 24.

Point Guards

Stephen Curry, Chris Paul, Russell Westbrook, Damian Lillard, Kyrie Irving, Derrick Rose, Jeff Teague, Deron Williams, Elfrid Payton, Tony Parker, Mike Conley, John Wall. (If the player you would like to name is not listed, add his name.)

Shooting Guards

James Harden, Kobe Bryant, Dwyane Wade, Jimmy Butler, Klay Thompson, Manu Ginobili, J.J. Redick, Wesley Matthews, Isaiah Thomas, Bradley Beal, DeMar DeRozan, Khris Middleton. (If the player you would like to name is not listed, add his name.)

Small Forwards

Kevin Durant, Kawhi Leonard, Lebron James, Carmelo Anthony, Paul George, Luol Deng, DeMarre Carroll, Andrew Wiggins, Rudy Gay, Tobias Harris, Gordon Hayward, Chandler Parsons. (If the player you would like to name is not listed, add his name.)

Power Forwards

Kevin Love, LaMarcus Aldridge, Blake Griffin, Anthony Davis, Chris Bosh, Kenneth Faried, Dirk Nowitzki, Paul Millsap, Zach Randolph, Draymond Green, Pau Gasol, Derrick Favors, Tim Duncan. (If the player you would like to name is not listed, add his name.)

Centers

Marc Gasol, Joakim Noah, DeMarcus Cousins, Dwight Howard, DeAndre Jordan, Brook Lopez, Andre Drummond, Al Jefferson, Greg Monroe, Nikola Vucevic, Rudy Gobert, Tyson Chandler. (If the player you would like to name is not listed, add his name.)

Point Guards

——————————, ——————————,
——————————, ——————————,
——————————

Shooting Guards:

——————————, ——————————,
——————————, ——————————,
——————————

Small Forwards:

——————————, ——————————,
——————————, ——————————,
——————————

Power Forwards:

——————————, ——————————,
——————————, ——————————,
——————————

Centers:

——————————, ——————————,
——————————, ——————————,
——————————

Your Starting 5 Players

Point Guard

Shooting Guard

Small Forward

Power Forward

Center

Kentrell's Picks

1. Who is your favorite basketball player?

Lebron James

2. Who is your favorite basketball team?

Cleveland Cavs

3. Name your 5 favorite players.

Lebron James, Anthony Davis, Chris Paul, Stephen Curry, Kawhi Leonard

4. Who do you think will win the NBA championship this year?

Cleveland Cavs

5. Why?

Because they have Lebron James and great players around him.

6. Who will win the MVP this year?

Stephen Curry

My 5 Favorite Players by Position

Point Guard

Stephen Curry, Russell Westbrook, Kyrie Irving, Chris Paul, Derrick Rose

Shooting Guard

James Harden, Kobe Bryant, Dwayne Wade, Jimmy Butler, Clay Thompson

Small Forward

Kevin Durant, Lebron James, Kawhi Leonard, Carmelo Anthony, Paul George

Power Forward

Kevin Love, LaMarcus Aldridge, Blake Griffin, Anthony Davis, Chris Bosh

Center

Marc Gasol, Joakim Noah, DeMarcus Cousins, Andre Drummond, DeAndre Jordan

My Starting 5 Players

Point Guard

Stephen Curry

Shooting Guard

Jimmy Butler

Small Forward

Lebron James

Power Forward

Anthony Davis

Center

Joakim Noah

Basketball Types

Types of passes

Overhead pass
Chest pass
Baseball pass
Bounce pass
Behind the back
No look

Types of shots

Layup
Jump shot
Hook shot
Bank shot
Floater
Reverse
Dunk

Types of Defenses

Man-to-man

Zone

Types of Zone Defenses

2-3 zone
3-2 zone
1-3-1 zone
Box and 1
Triangle and 2
2-2-1 zone
1-2-2 zone
1-1-2-1 zone

The diagram on the next page shows
the spots on a basketball court
that you should know.

The Basketball Court

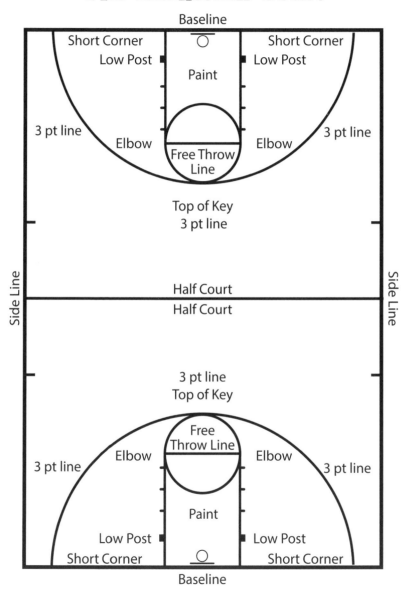

Hand Signs

On the following pages,
Kasey demonstrates 10 signs for
basketball terms and other frequently
used words used in this story.

Visit the Shelly's Adventures
YouTube page at
https://youtube.com/user/ShellysAdventuresLLC
for an interactive tutorial.

EXCITED

Move both hands in a
circular motion, tapping
your chest each time.
(Look excited.)

FUN

Move two fingers from your nose onto the top of the two fingers in front of you.

FORGOT

Hold your hand close to your forehead. Then move the hand away from your forehead and change your hand-shape into an "a."

PLAY

Both hands make the "y" shape. Twist them back and forth.

PRACTICE

Move the top hand with the sideways "a" shape left and right on top of the index finger.

TODAY

With both hands making the "y" shape, bring both hands down twice (with a slight bounce).

BASKETBALL

Make two quick
up-and-down movements
with your hands.

40

GAME

Make both hands into a fist with your thumbs sticking up. Then tap your fist together.

COACH

With the "c" shape,
tap the top of your
shoulder.

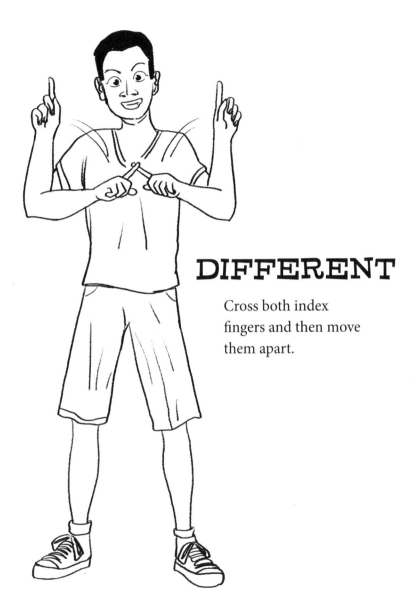

DIFFERENT

Cross both index
fingers and then move
them apart.

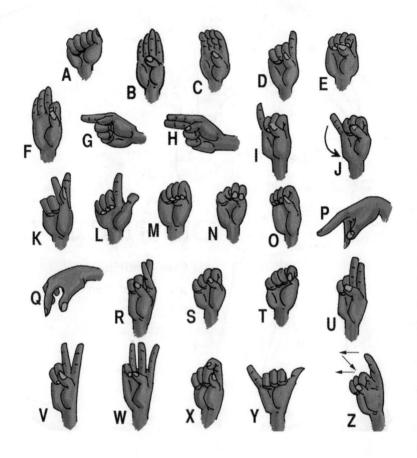

Glossary

Assist: Pass the ball to a teammate who scores.

Baseball pass: Throw a pass with one hand (like a baseball pass).

Block shot: Knock the ball out of the air when an opponent is trying to shoot it into the hoop.

Bounce pass: A pass in which the ball is bounced off of the floor.

Box out: Prevent an opponent from getting a rebound.

Call the pick/screen: Warn your teammate that someone is trying to pick/set a screen on him or her.

Chest pass: A pass made with two hands from the chest.

Cut: Run towards the basketball goal when your teammate has the ball.

Defense: Prevent your opponents from scoring the basketball in the hoop.

Defensive drills: Drills to help players improve their defense.

Deny the ball: Prevent the opposing player from getting the ball.

Dribble: Continuously bounce the ball with one hand.

Double dribble: Dribble the ball with two hands; or dribble the ball with one hand, pick it up with two hands, and then dribble again with one hand.

Double team: Two people on defense guard one player on offense.

Free throw: A free shot attempt from the free throw line. It's worth one point.

Foul: Illegally have physical contact with an opposing player.

Four-on-four: Four offensive players play against four defensive players.

Half court: One half of the court. The halves are split by the half court line.

High post: Area on the court near the free-throw line.

Jumpshot/jumper: Jump in the air while attempting to shoot the ball through the basketball hoop.

Layup: Attempt to shoot the ball from a close distance.

Low post: Area on the court right under the basketball hoop (typically by the boxes closest to the hoop).

Man-to-man: Play defense against one person on the opposing team.

One-on-one: Play against only one person from the opposing team.

Overhead pass: A pass made with two hands. The player passes the ball from above the top of his or her head.

Offense: Circumstance of the team that has the basketball.

Offensive drills: Drills to practice offense.

Paint lane: The area in the box in front of the basketball goal.

Pass: Throw the ball to another player on the same team.

Pick/set a screen: Block the defender from the offensive player he or she is guarding.

Pick & roll: Pick/set a screen and then run towards the basket hoop.

Pivot: Keep one foot on the ground while turning around.

Press: Guard a player tightly.

Possession: Circumstance of a team having the ball.

Pump fake: Act as if you are going to shoot or pass.

Rebound: Grab the ball when it fails to go through the hoop/basket.

Shoot: Attempt to make the ball go through the hoop/basket by throwing it.

Steal: Intercept the ball from an offensive player on the opposing team.

Travel: Take too many steps while carrying the ball. (A player carrying the ball is allowed only two steps without dribbling.)

Turnover: When the team with the ball loses possession of the ball.

Zone defense: Guarding a certain area on the court instead of guarding a player on the opposing team.

About the Authors

KENTRELL MARTIN is the author of books for children in the **Shelly's Adventures Series**.

As a child, Kentrell played many different sports, but basketball was his favorite. He even played at the collegiate level at the University of New Orleans. That's why he decided to make the first book in the **Kasey Plays Sports** sub-series about basketball.

When asked what he hopes children will learn from this book, Kentrell replied, "I hope children learn the primary lesson taught in the book—Be yourself!—along with the 10 American Sign Language (ASL) signs that are introduced at the end of the story. And I hope that every person who picks up *Kasey's First*

Day of Basketball Practice enjoys the book from start to finish."

If you think that your starting five can beat Kentrell's starting five, send him an email at kentrell@shellysadventures.com and tell him why. He will reply to you.

KENTRELL MARTIN, JR., the eldest son of author Kentrell Martin, goes by the nickname, KJ. This is KJ's first book, but he plans to write many more. When KJ isn't playing sports or spending time with his family, he enjoys reading and writing plays.